BASTIEN PIANO BASICS

PIANO

PRIMER LEVEL

BY JAMES BASTIEN

KJOS NEIL A. KJOS MUSIC COMPANY • SAN DIEGO, CALIFORNIA

Dear teachers and parents:

BASTIEN PIANO BASICS is an exciting and comprehensive series for piano study designed to get the young student off to the right start. The learning sequence is carefully graded to assure steady progress, while the full-color illustrations entertain and reinforce along the way. The selection of pieces includes original works as well as familiar folk songs and pop styles in creative, enjoyable arrangements.

A gradual multi-key approach is used allowing the student to experience complete keyboard knowledge. The student will learn basic rhythm patterns, intervals, chords, scales, and essential signs and terms. All three core books—**Piano, Theory,** and **Performance**—are coordinated page-by-page (see *Contents*) to provide thorough reinforcement of basic concepts at each level. The **Bastien Music Flashcards** may be introduced with page 26. The **Bastien Music Notebook,** an assignment book, may be used starting with the first lesson.

BASTIEN PIANO BASICS is a method designed for achievement and success. We offer you our best wishes for the rich rewards music can bring to each child's life.

Neil A. Kjos Music Company
James Bastien
Jane Smisor Bastien

ISBN 0-8497-5265-5

Contents

*To reinforce the feeling of achievement, the teacher or student may put a √ when the page has been mastered.

Sitting at the Piano

■ Sit up straight facing the center of the piano. Place your feet flat on the floor. If your feet do not reach the floor, it is helpful to have a footstool or books under them when you practice.

■ Sit high enough to reach the keys easily. Do you have a piano stool or chair at home which moves up and down? If not, cushions or books may be used to help you sit at the correct height when you practice.

Hand Position

■ Hold your fingers in a nice **curved shape**. Imagine you are holding a ball in each hand. That is the way the fingers should be curved when playing the piano. Your wrists should be level with your arms.

9-25-90
REVIEW p. 4-15
LEARN p. 16-19 (24)

Finger Numbers

3
4
2
1
5

2
3
1
4
5

**Left Hand
(L.H.)**

**Right Hand
(R.H.)**

Pencil Play

Draw an outline of your hands on a piece of paper. Number each finger.

Practice Directions

Hold up your hands and wiggle your fingers.

- Wiggle your **first** fingers (thumbs).
- Wiggle your **second** fingers.
- Wiggle your **third** (middle) fingers.
- Wiggle your **fourth** fingers.
- Wiggle your **fifth** (little) fingers.

Your teacher, or someone in your family, can name
fingers for you to wiggle in either hand.

The Piano Keyboard

The keyboard has **white** and **black** keys.
The black keys are in sets of **2**'s and **3**'s.

← —— **Down** ——   **Up** —— →

Practice Directions

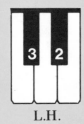

L.H.

1. Play the sets of 2 black keys with your L.H. Play both keys **together** up and down the keyboard. Next, play the keys **one at a time** saying "play up" or "play down."

2. Play the sets of 2 black keys with your R.H. Play both keys **together** up and down the keyboard. Next, play the keys **one at a time** saying "play up" or "play down."

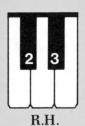

R.H.

3. Play the sets of 3 black keys with your L.H. Play the keys **together** up and down the keyboard. Next, play the keys **one at a time** saying "playing up" or "playing down."

4. Play the sets of 3 black keys with your R.H. Play the keys **together** up and down the keyboard. Next, play the keys **one at a time**, saying "playing up" or "playing down."

R.H.

Low and High

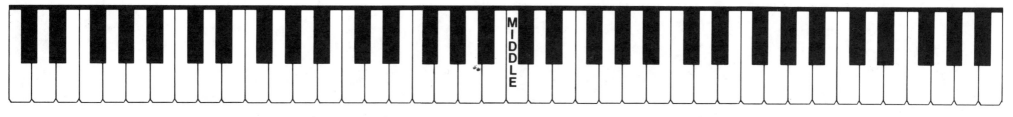

Low   **High**

When you play **down** to the left on the keyboard, the sounds are **lower**.

When you play **up** to the right on the keyboard, the sounds are **higher**.

1. With your L.H., play 2 low black keys.

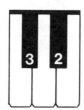

2. With your R.H., play 2 middle black keys.

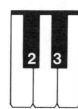

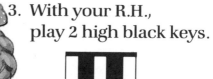

3. With your R.H., play 2 high black keys.

4. With your L.H., play 3 low black keys.

5. With your L.H., play 3 middle black keys.

6. With your R.H., play 3 high black keys.

Rhythm in Music

1. Music has a pattern of **short** and **long** tones. The combination of these tones written in notes is called **rhythm**.

Quarter note

Count: quar-ter

Half note

Count: half note

2. Notes are divided by **bar lines** into **measures**.

Bar line

Bar line

Measure

Measure

Double bar line
used at the end
of a piece

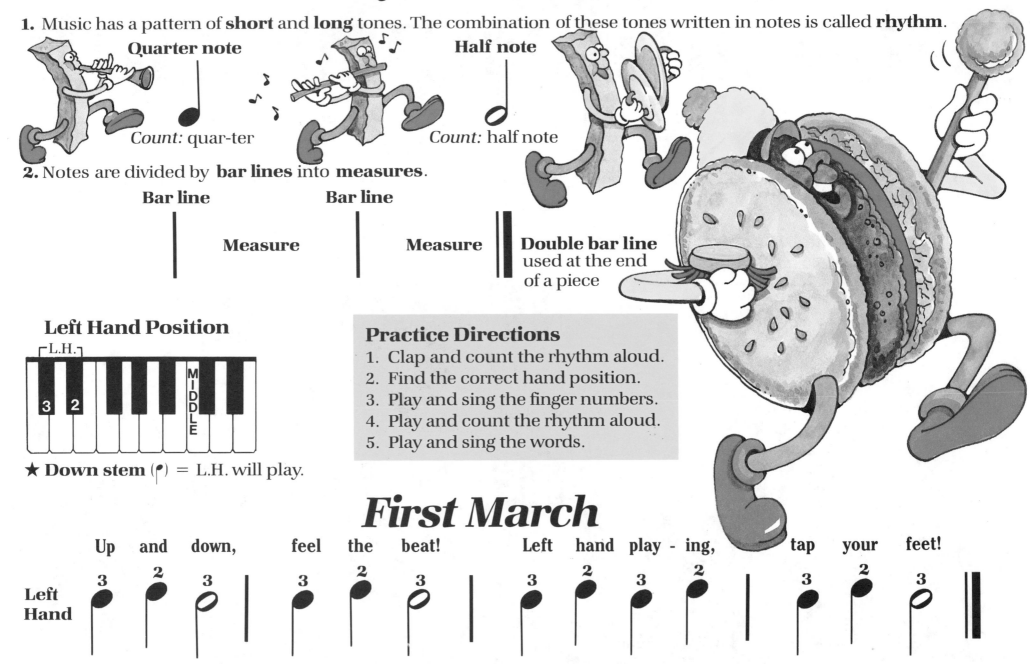

Left Hand Position

★ **Down stem** (♩) = L.H. will play.

Practice Directions
1. Clap and count the rhythm aloud.
2. Find the correct hand position.
3. Play and sing the finger numbers.
4. Play and count the rhythm aloud.
5. Play and sing the words.

First March

Up and down, feel the beat! Left hand play - ing, tap your feet!

Left
Hand
3 2 3 3 2 3 3 2 3 2 3 2 3

★ Follow the Practice Directions on page 8.

Right Hand Position

★ **Up stem** ($\downarrow$) = R.H. will play.

The Balloon Man

Right Hand

In his right hand   way up high,

2 3 4 3   2 3 4

Red bal - loons fly   in the sky!

4 3 2 3   4 3 2

WP200

Whole Note

o

Count: whole note hold it

Position for Hands

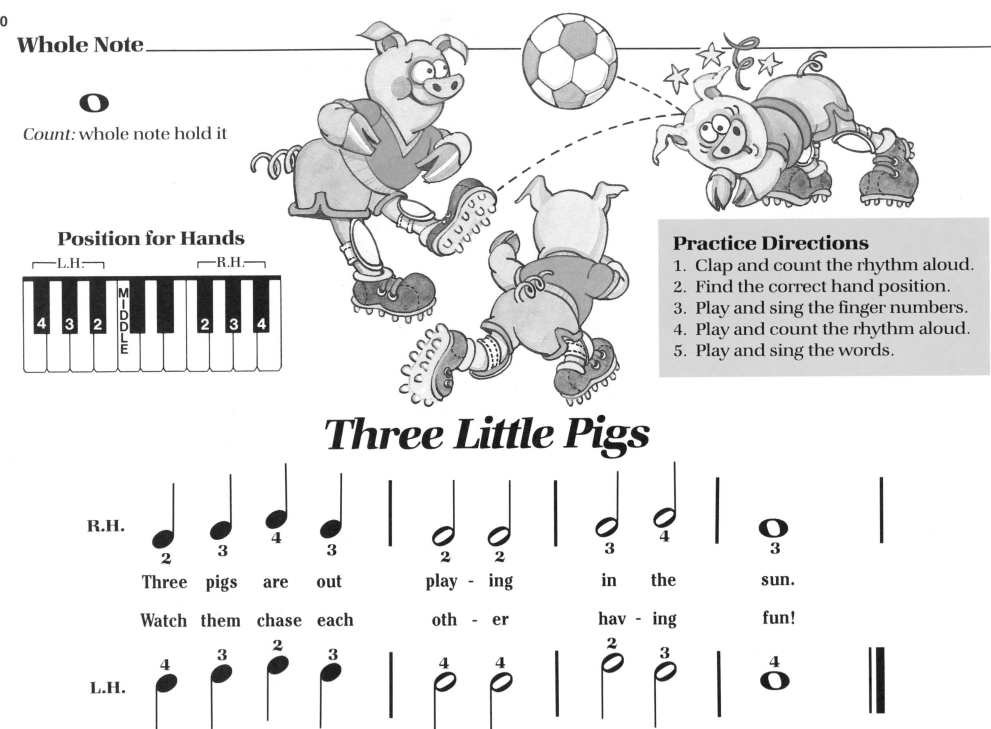

Practice Directions
1. Clap and count the rhythm aloud.
2. Find the correct hand position.
3. Play and sing the finger numbers.
4. Play and count the rhythm aloud.
5. Play and sing the words.

Three Little Pigs

R.H.

2   3   4   3   2   2   3   4   3

Three   pigs   are   out   play - ing   in   the   sun.

Watch   them   chase   each   oth - er   hav - ing   fun!

L.H.

4   3   2   3   4   4   2   3   4

Repeat Dots :‖

The two dots at the end of the piece are a **repeat sign**, meaning to play again from the beginning.

Position for Hands

★ Follow the Practice Directions on page 10.

Lamb at School

R.H.

3 2 1 2   3 3 3   2 2 2   3 5 5

1. On the way to   school one day,   school one day,   school one day,
2. In the class it   caused a scene,   caused a scene,   caused a scene,

On the way to   school one day,   Mar - y met a   lamb.
In the class it   caused a scene,   teach - er gave a   scream!

1 2 3 2   1 1 1   2 2 1 2   3

L.H.

Duet Part (Student part to be played one octave higher.)

R.H.

L.H.

stacc.

1.   2.

WP200

Position for Hands

Old MacDonald

R.H.

				3	3	2	2	**O** **1**

1. Old Mac - Don - ald   had   a   farm,   E - I - E - I -   O!
2. On this farm he   had   a   chick,   E - I - E - I -   O!

L.H.

Duet Part (Student part to be played one octave higher.)

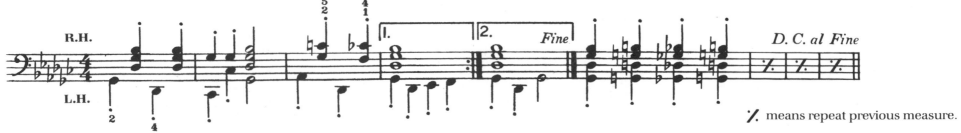

𝄍 means repeat previous measure.

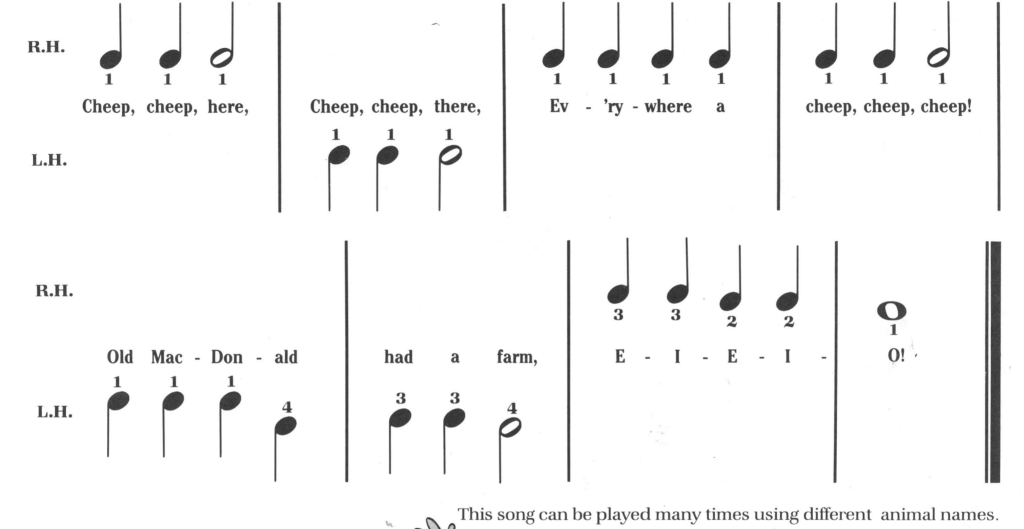

R.H.

Cheep, cheep, here,

Cheep, cheep, there,

Ev - 'ry - where a

cheep, cheep, cheep!

L.H.

R.H.

Old Mac - Don - ald

had a farm,

E - I - E - I -

O!

L.H.

This song can be played many times using different animal names.

The Music Alphabet

The music alphabet is made of **seven** letters.

These same letters are used over and over on the keyboard to name the **white** keys.

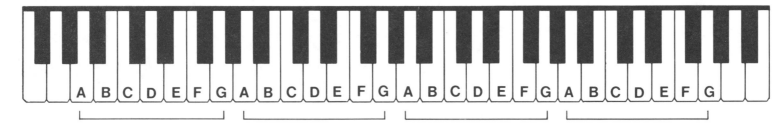

When you play and say the music alphabet forward, you go **up** the keyboard to the **right**.

Up the keyboard ⟶

When you play and say the music alphabet backward, you go **down** the keyboard to the **left**.

⟵ **Down** the keyboard

Practice Directions
1. Play the music alphabet both forward and backward in different places on the keyboard, using the second finger of either hand. Say the letters aloud as you play.
2. **Memorize** the music alphabet forward and backward.

White Keys

It is easy to find the **white keys** and know their names when you look for the sets of 2 and 3 black keys.

Practice Directions
1. Find and play the following keys on your piano. Play all the A's, B's, C's, D's, E's, F's, G's. Use any finger.
2. Memorize the location of each key.

A is between the 2nd and 3rd black keys in the 3 black key set.

B is to the right of the 3 black key set.

C is to the left of the 2 black key set.

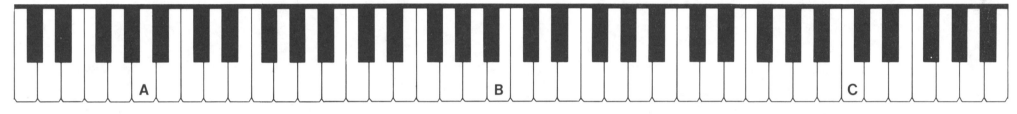

D is in the middle of the 2 black key set.

E is to the right of the 2 black key set.

F is to the left of the 3 black key set.

G is between the 1st and 2nd black keys in the 3 black key set.

Practice Directions
1. Shut your eyes.
2. Touch sets of 2 and 3 black keys with one hand. With the other hand find and name nearby white keys.
3. Memorize a picture of the keyboard!

Playing Legato

Legato means to play smoothly, connecting the tones. To play legato, one finger lifts when another finger plays the next note.

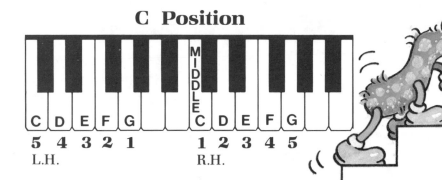

C Position

5 4 3 2 1   1 2 3 4 5
L.H.   R.H.

Practice Directions
1. Clap and count the rhythm aloud.
2. Find the correct hand position.
3. Play and sing the finger numbers aloud.
4. Play and name the notes aloud.
5. Play and count the rhythm aloud.
6. Play and sing the words.

Stepping Up and Down

Play legato

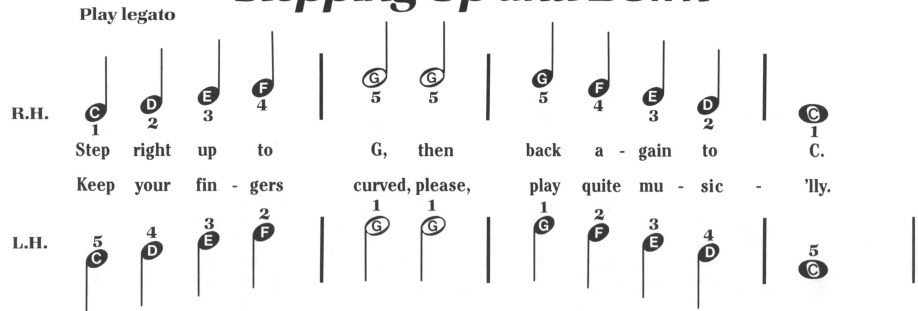

R.H.

Step right up to   G, then   back a - gain to   C.

Keep your fin - gers   curved, please, play quite mu - sic -   'lly.

L.H.

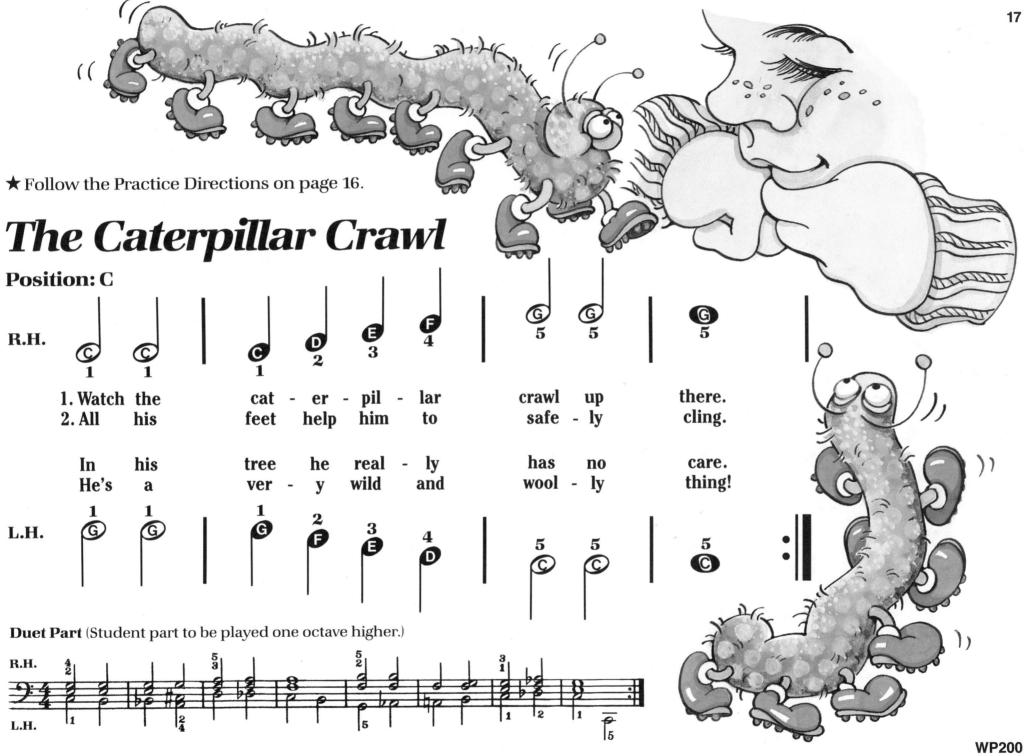

Time Signature

The **time signature** is the two numbers written at the beginning of a piece. The **top** number tells how many beats are in each measure. The **bottom** number tells what kind of note gets one beat.

2 means two beats in each measure.
4 means the quarter note gets one beat.

★ Clap and count this rhythm.

2
4

Count: 1   2   1   2
or: quar-ter quar-ter   half note

Practice Directions
1. Play and name the notes aloud.
2. Play and count the rhythm aloud.
3. Play and sing the words.

Express Train

Position: C

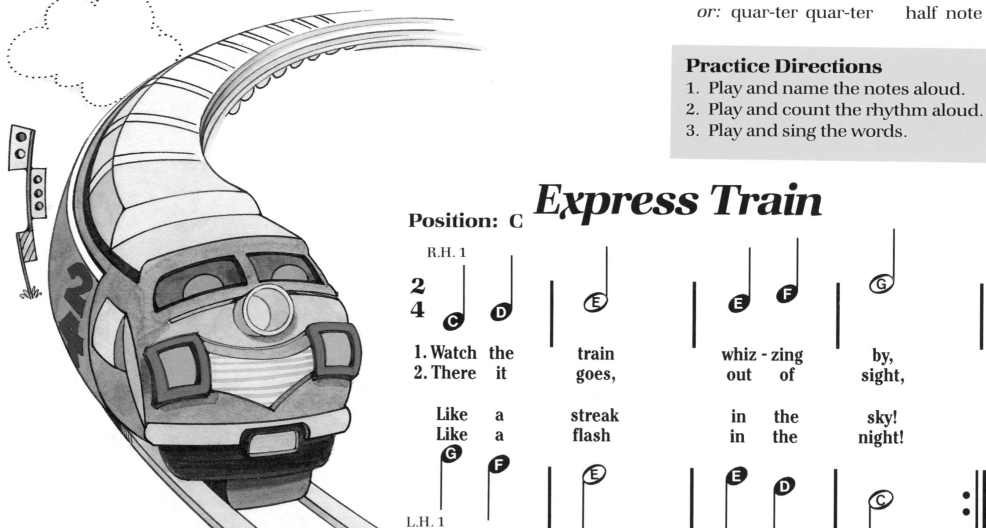

Our Monkey Bars

Position: C

1. On our mon - key bars we play,
2. Watch your foot - work, step with care,

Get - ting fit in ev - 'ry way.
Dan - ger may be wait - ing there!

Duet Part (Student part to be played one octave higher.)

Dotted Half Note

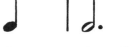

2+1 = 3 beats   A **dot** after a note adds half the value of the note.

3 means three beats in each measure.
4 means the quarter note gets one beat.

★ Clap and count this rhythm.

Count: 1   2   3   1   2   3
or: quar-ter quar-ter quar-ter half note dot

Practice Directions
1. Play and name the notes aloud.
2. Play and count the rhythm aloud.
3. Play and sing the words.

Backyard Bell

Position: C

R.H. 1

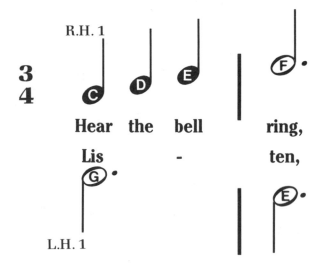

Hear the bell   ring,   Call - ing to   me,
Lis   -   ten,   as   it strikes three.

L.H. 1

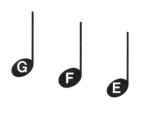
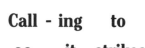

Imitate 3 bell rings on the piano.

Bike Ride

Position: C

R.H. 1

3
4

C E G | F E D | C D E | D.

1. It's just the sort of a day for a ride,
2. Rid - ing a - long on a bright sun - ny day,

Whiz - zing a - long with my pal at my side!
Off to the ball park where we will all play!

G E C | D E F | G G E | C.

L.H. 1

Duet Part (Student part to be played one octave higher.)

R.H.

L.H. *stacc.*

4 means four beats in each measure.
4 means the quarter note gets one beat.

★Clap and count this rhythm.

Count:	1	2	3	4	1	2	3	4
or:	quar-ter	quar-ter	half note		whole note		hold	it

Practice Directions
1. Play and name the notes aloud.
2. Play and count the rhythm aloud.
3. Play and sing the words.

Space Flight!

Position: C

1. As - tro - nauts,   space suits   on,   read - y   for   the   flight,
2. Off   it   goes,   far   a - way,   at   a   light - ning   pace,

Climb   a - board,   hear the count,   blast off   in   the   night!
Way   past Mars,   Ve - nus   too,   in - to   out - er   space!

Circus Fun

Position: C

1. Let's go to the cir - cus, see the big show.
2. Ac - ro - bats and clowns are there to greet you.

L.H. 5
R.H. 1

Look at all the acts lined up in a row!
El - e - phants and li - ons, bears, hors - es, too!

Duet Part (Student part to be played one octave higher.)

WP200

Review

1. Name these keys.

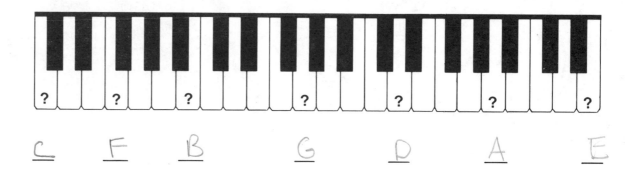

C   F   B   G   D   A   E

2. Write the names of the notes in the C position. C, D, E, F, G

3. Draw four quarter notes. ♩♩♩♩   4. Draw four half notes. ♩ ♩ ♩ ♩

5. Draw four dotted half notes. ♩. ♩. ♩. ♩.   6. Draw four whole notes. ○ ○ ○○

7. Clap and count this rhythm. 𝄞 4/4 ♩ ♩ ♩ | ♩. ♩ ♩ ♩ ♩ ♩ ♩ | ○ 𝄂

8. Name the following notes.   ○   ♩   ♩.   ♩

whole   quarter   dotted half   half

9. In a time signature the top number tells how many __beats__ in a measure;

the bottom number tells what kind of note gets __1__ beat.

10-2-90
P.25-31

Staffs and Clefs

1. Music is written on lines and spaces called a **staff**.

A staff has **five** lines and **four** spaces.

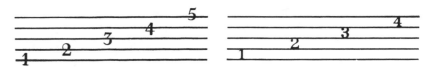

2. Notes are written on **lines**, or in **spaces**.

3. Piano music uses **two clefs**.

This is a **treble clef**, 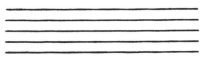 This is a **bass clef**,
or **G clef** sign: or **F clef** sign:

4. **High** tones are written on a **treble staff**.

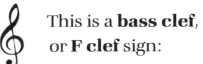

Low tones are written on a **bass staff**.

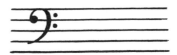

How Notes Move On the Staff

Notes move on the staff in three ways:

Step   **Skip**   **Repeat**

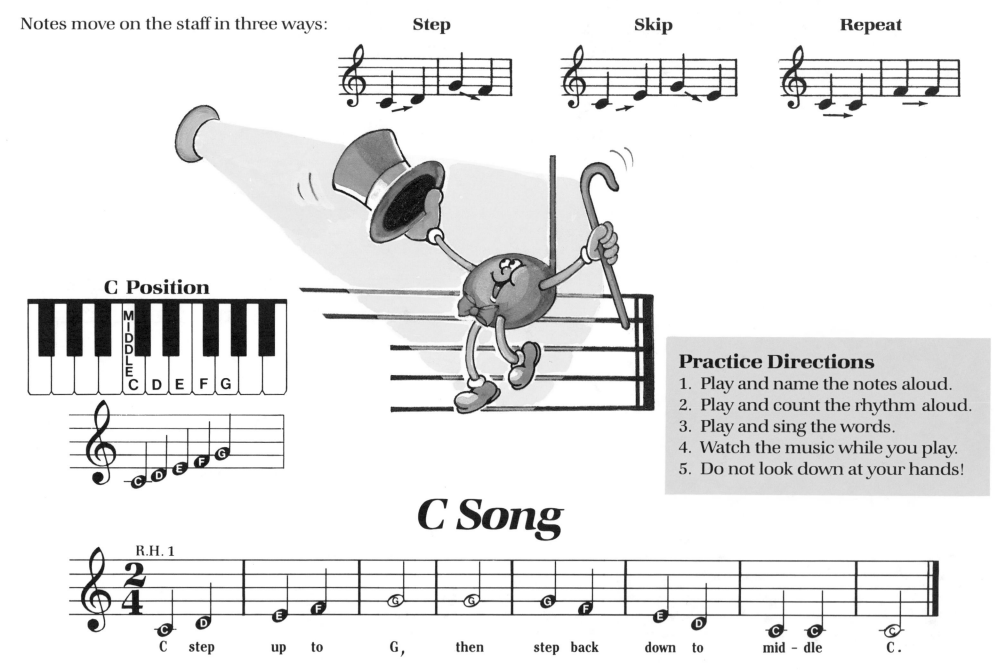

C Position

MIDDLE C D E F G

C D E F G

Practice Directions
1. Play and name the notes aloud.
2. Play and count the rhythm aloud.
3. Play and sing the words.
4. Watch the music while you play.
5. Do not look down at your hands!

C Song

R.H. 1

C step up to G, then step back down to mid - dle C.

Teacher: The student is ready for **Bastien Music Flashcards**. Sort out and assign notes introduced in this lesson. Assign new cards as new notes are introduced.

Skipping Fingers

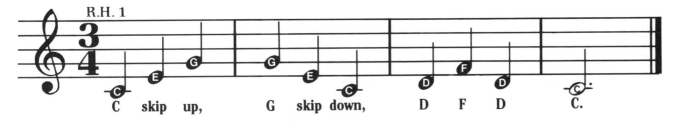

Easy Repeats

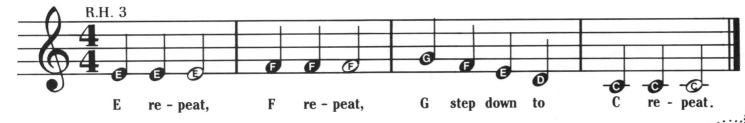

Go Tell Aunt Rhodie

Direction of Stems

Notes on or above the middle line have **down** stems. Notes below the middle line have **up** stems.

Down stems   Up stems

C Position

Practice Directions ❋
1. Play and name the notes aloud.
2. Play and count the rhythm aloud.
3. Play and sing the words.

Skating

L.H. 5

C   skate   up   to   G,   then   skate back   down to   low – er   C.

❋**Teacher:** Have the student follow these practice directions throughout the book.

Roller Coaster Ride

L.H. 5
Up we go, down we go, fast and then slow.

Boat Ride

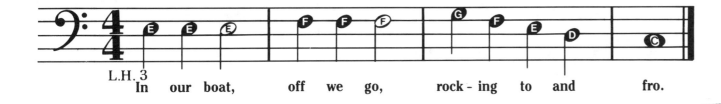

L.H. 3
In our boat, off we go, rock-ing to and fro.

Ode to Joy

L.H. 3
Lis-ten to this mel-o-dy of glad-ness sound-ing joy-ful-ly!

Play it with a spe-cial feel-ing, as it rings tri-um-phant-ly!

The Grand Staff

The bass and treble staffs are joined together by a **brace** to form the **grand staff.**

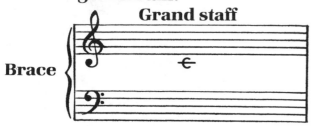

A short line is added between the staffs for middle C.

C Position

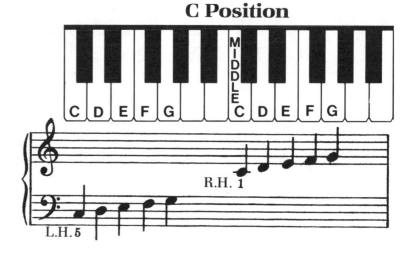

C Warm-up

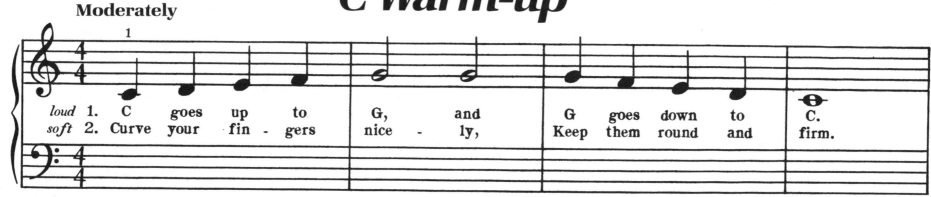

Moderately

loud 1.	C	goes	up	to	G,	and	G	goes	down	to	C.
soft 2.	Curve	your	fin -	gers	nice -	ly,	Keep	them	round	and	firm.

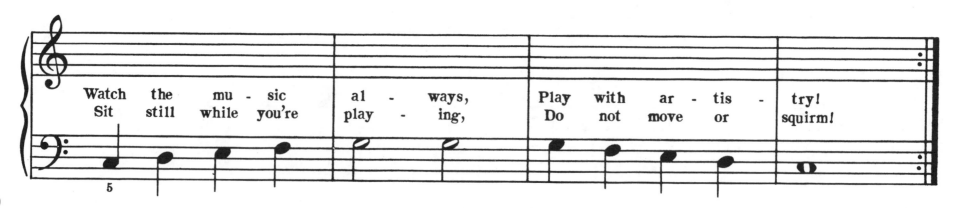

Watch	the	mu -	sic	al -	ways,	Play	with	ar -	tis -	try!
Sit	still	while	you're	play -	ing,	Do	not	move	or	squirm!

Playing Loud and Soft

Music has **loud** and **soft** signs called **dynamics**.

f means **loud**. Its Italian name is *forte*.
p means **soft**. Its Italian name is *piano*.

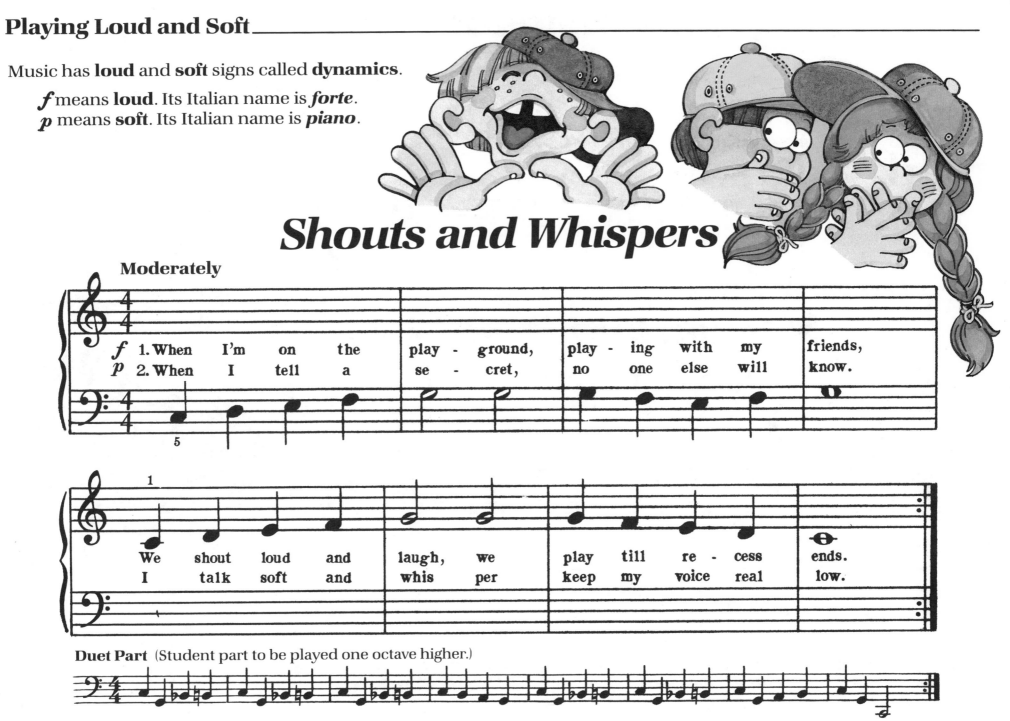

Shouts and Whispers

Duet Part (Student part to be played one octave higher.)

WP200

10-9-90
p.32-43

Measuring Intervals

The distance between two notes is called an **interval**.

2nd

On the keys a **2nd** is like a **step**: from one key to the next key.

2nd

On the staff a **2nd** is like a **step**: from line to space or space to line.

Up by 2nds   Down by 2nds

★ What intervals are used in this piece?

Stealing 2nd Base

Moderately

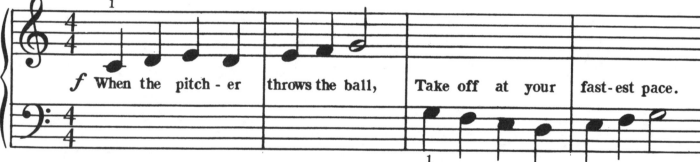

f When the pitch-er │ throws the ball, │ Take off at your │ fast-est pace.

May-be if you │ have some luck, │ You can steal │ sec-ond base!

WP200

3rd

On the keys a **3rd** is like a **skip**: skip a key.

On the staff a **3rd** is like a **skip:** from line to line or space to space.

★ Find the 3rds in this piece.

Up by 3rds　　　　Down by 3rds

Skipping Frogs

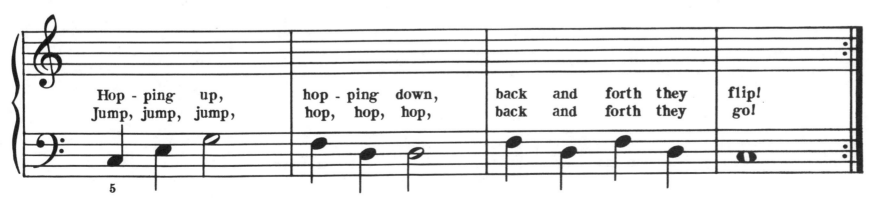

Moderately

f
1. See   the   frogs   jump - ing   there,   watch them   now   as   they   skip.
2. First   one   jumps,   then   one   hops,   jump - ing   frogs   in   a   row.

Hop - ping   up,   hop - ping   down,   back   and   forth   they   flip!
Jump, jump, jump,   hop, hop, hop,   back   and   forth   they   go!

Slur

A **slur** is a curved line over or under two or more notes that are to be played legato (smooth, connected). The slur is used to show a musical thought called a **phrase**.

Hal - low - een will soon be here

Phrase (musical thought)

★ Lift your hand gently at the end of a phrase.

Happy Halloween

Spookily

1. Hal - low - een will soon be here, From the trees, ghosts will peer!
2. Trick or treat - ing we will go, Knock on doors, say hel - lo!

Pump - kins smile a - long the way, It's a ver - y spec - ial day!
Find a cos - tume that's just right. We'll have fun this spook - y night!

Duet Part (Student part to be played one octave higher.)

R.H.

L.H.

Tied Notes

A **tie** is a curved line which connects notes on the **same** line or space. Play the first note only and hold it for the value of both notes.

★ Find the 2nds and 3rds in this piece.

Hold, do not play again.

Count: 1 2 3 1 2 3

Noah's Ark

Moderately

f
1. When the rains came pour - ing down from the sky,
2. When the flood end - ed, and out came the sun,

No - ah's Ark kept them all dry._____
They all went out and had fun!_____

Duet Part (Student part to be played one octave higher.)

R.H.

L.H. *stacc.*

4th

On the keys a **4th** is a larger **skip:** skip two keys.

On the staff a **4th** is a larger **skip:** from line to space or space to line.

Up by 4ths   Down by 4ths

★ Find the 4ths in this piece.

Four Funny Clowns

Moderately

f
1. Clowns are fun - ny   don't you know,   They will try to   steal the show.
2. Watch them spin - ning   to and fro,   Run - ning, danc - ing,   on tip - toe.

Twist - ing, turn - ing,   in a row,   On their bikes and   off they go!
When they end the   fun - ny show,   On their bikes and   off they go!

★ Name the intervals in this piece.

Boogie Beat

Bright boogie tempo

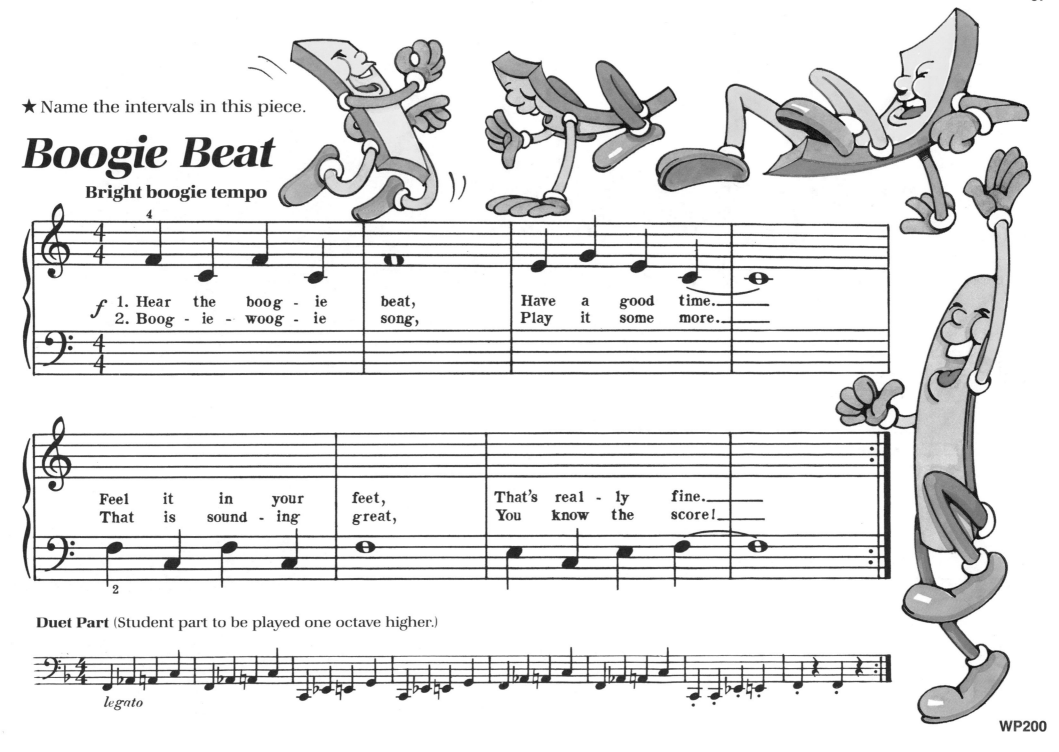

Duet Part (Student part to be played one octave higher.)

legato

5th

On the keys a **5th** is a larger **skip:** skip three keys.

On the staff a **5th** is a larger **skip:** from line to line or space to space.

Up a 5th   Down a 5th

★ Find the 5ths in this piece.

Five Hunting Hounds

Brightly

f 1. I hear a fifth sound - ing near - by to me.
p 2. Five hounds are run - ning to catch the old fox.

It is a hunt - ing horn, that I now see.
He is out hid - ing there un - der a box!

Melodic and Harmonic Intervals

A **melodic** interval has single notes, like notes in a melody.

A **harmonic** interval has two notes together, to make harmony in music.

★ Name the kinds of intervals in this piece.

Indian Drums

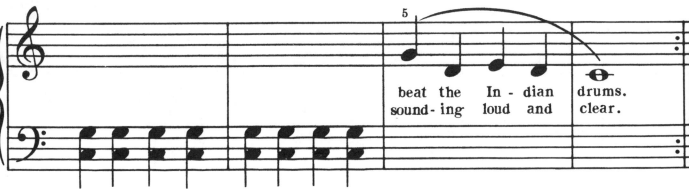

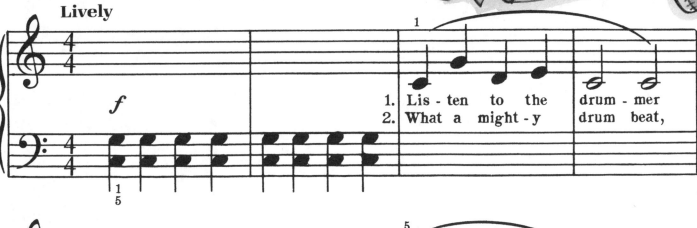

Sept.
Watch
Notes

Rest Signs

Rest signs are used in music for **silence**. Each note has a rest sign of the same value.

Quarter note ♩ = 1 beat   Half note ♪ = 2 beats   Whole note 𝅝 = 4 beats
rest 𝄽 = 1 beat   rest ▬ = 2 beats   rest ▬ = 4 beats, or a whole measure

★ Name the rests here and on page 41.

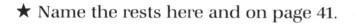

My Computer

Happily

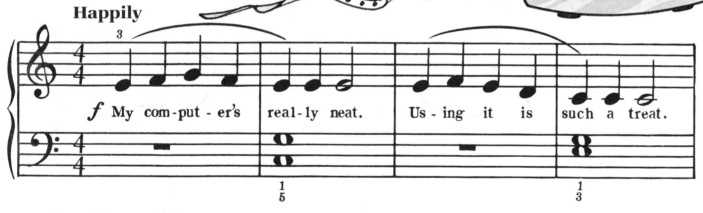

f My com-put-er's   real-ly neat.   Us-ing it is   such a treat.

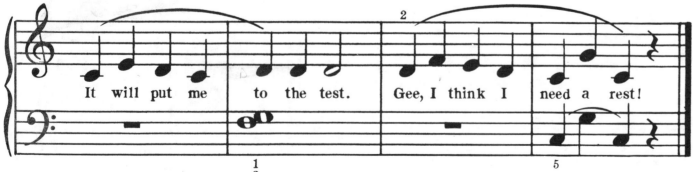

It will put me   to the test.   Gee, I think I   need a rest!

WP200

Playing C Chords

The **C chord** is formed from **three** of the keys in the C position: C   E   G

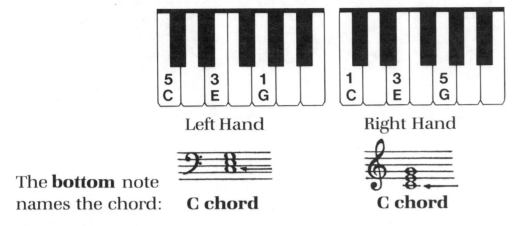

Left Hand

Right Hand

The **bottom** note
names the chord: **C chord**   **C chord**

1. **Solid chord:** notes played together

(Play 1st time *f*, 2nd time *p*.)

f - p

2. **Broken chord:** notes played one at a time

f - p

★ Play the L.H. softer than the R.H. melody.

Row, Row, Row Your Boat

Moderately fast

Row, row, row your boat, gent-ly down the stream.

Mer - ri - ly, mer - ri - ly, mer - ri - ly, mer - ri - ly, life is but a dream.

To feel the boat rocking in the waves, play this left hand part as you sing the words.
Can you play it as you play the melody?

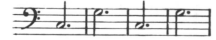

Love Somebody

Happily

f

1. Love some-bod-y, 'deed I do! Love some-bod-y, yes I do!
2. Who's the one that I like best? Some-one ver-y near to me.

Love some-bod-y, 'deed I do! I won't tell, I won't say who!
I might tell who it may be. You're the one, oh can't you see!

10-16-90
p. 44-51

Middle C Position

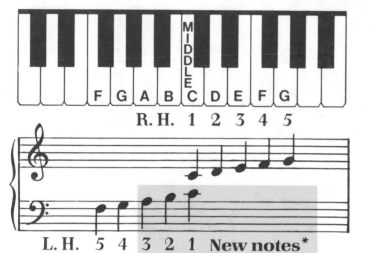

R. H. 1 2 3 4 5

L. H. 5 4 3 2 1 New notes*

Practice Directions
1. Place both thumbs on middle C.
2. Keep your eyes on the book.
3. Play and name the L.H. notes.

Middle C Warm-up

Moderately

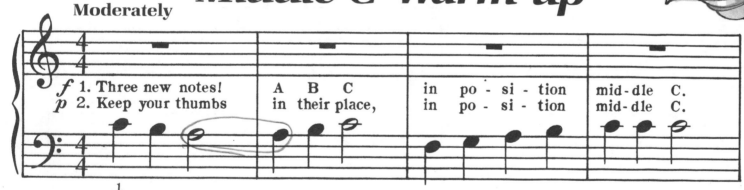

f 1. Three new notes!   A   B   C   in po - si - tion   mid - dle   C.
p 2. Keep your thumbs   in their place,   in po - si - tion   mid - dle   C.

Right hand thumb   on   C   too,   Same old notes here   for re - view!
When you read   ev - 'ry   day,   Watch the book, please,   as you play!

*__Teacher:__ Sort out these notes from the **Bastien Music Flashcards** and assign with this lesson.

I'm a Little Teapot

Two Eighth Notes

Two eighth notes equal one quarter note.

Clap and count: 1 and 2 and | 1 and 2 and

or: two eighths quar-ter two eighths quar-ter

Birthday Fun

Brightly

f Birth-days come | once a year. | Mine will soon be | here!

We'll have fun | on that day. | We will sing and | play!

9-29

Skip to My Lou

Sharp Sign ♯

The **sharp sign** before a note means to play the next key to the **right**, which may be black or white.

★ Play the following sharp notes. Use the L.H. for the bass clef notes, the R.H. for the treble clef notes.

The Funny Snowman

Moderately

f 1. See the fun - ny snow-man there, he's jol - ly, fat, and round.
p 2. If the weath - er stays real cold, he'll stay the same ol' size.

He looks like he's laugh-ing, but he does-n't make a sound.
But when warm sun shines, he'll dis - ap - pear be - fore your eyes!

Lavender's Blue

WP200

Aura Lee

Slowly

p As the black-bird | in the spring, | 'neath the wil - low | tree, —

Sat and piped, I | heard him sing in | praise of Au - ra | Lee.

Duet Part (Student part to be played one octave higher.)

R.H.

L.H.

Scarborough Fair

Dec. 8

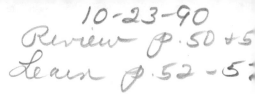

G Position

★ Play the notes above up and down saying their names.

G Warm-up

Moderately

f G po - si - tion's lots of fun, Keep your fin - gers in their place.

"G po - si - tion I've be - gun, I'll play e - ven, I won't race!"

Teacher: Sort out these notes from the **Bastien Music Flashcards** and assign with this lesson.

That Old Car

Dec. 15

Moderately fast

f (Beep beep beep, beep beep beep.) Off it goes there down the street in one gi-gan-tic leap.

(Beep beep beep, beep beep beep.) That old car is full of rust, it's real-ly quite a heap! (beep beep)

Thanksgiving Turkey

Moderately fast

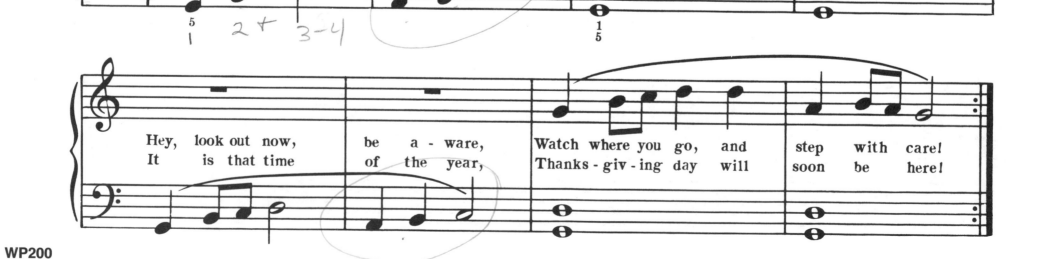

1. Out in the barn lives the bird, He's hid-ing there so he won't be heard.
2. It's get-ting cold day by day, Leaves turn-ing col - or, what a dis - play!

Hey, look out now, be a - ware, Watch where you go, and step with care!
It is that time of the year, Thanks - giv - ing day will soon be here!

WP200

A sharp note (♯) remains sharp for the whole measure.

C♯   still C♯

The Singing Donkey

Jan,

Lively

p Hear the don - key sing - in' at the break of day.

If no one will feed him, this is what he'll say: *f* "Hee -

haw! Hee - haw! Hee - haw, hee - haw, hee - haw!"

WP200

Playing Staccato

Staccato means to play short, separating the tones.

A **dot** over ♩ or under ♩ a note means staccato.

To play staccato, let the key go immediately after playing.

Staccato Warm-up

★ Play hands separately first; then play hands together.

The Clock

Lively

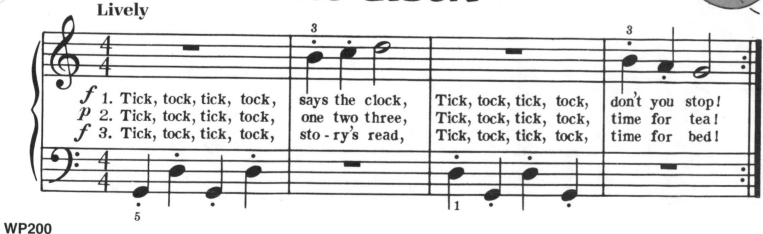

f 1. Tick, tock, tick, tock,   says the clock,   Tick, tock, tick, tock,   don't you stop!
p 2. Tick, tock, tick, tock,   one two three,   Tick, tock, tick, tock,   time for tea!
f 3. Tick, tock, tick, tock,   sto-ry's read,   Tick, tock, tick, tock,   time for bed!

Basketball

10-30-90
p. 58-63

Flat Sign ♭

The **flat sign** before a note means to play the next key to the **left**, which may be black or white.

★ Play the following flat notes. Use the L.H. for the bass clef notes, the R.H. for the treble clef notes.

Feb. 9th

Electric Bass

Fast rock

(move down)

WP200

The Dragon's Lair

Indian Dance

Lively

f Lit - tle In - dian, 'round the fire___ he would dance.

continue staccato

Lit - tle In - dian, do the In - dian dance.

continue staccato

Jingle Bells

Lively

Jin-gle bells, jin-gle bells, jin-gle all the way! Oh, what fun it is to ride in a one horse o-pen sleigh!

Jin-gle bells, jin-gle bells, jin-gle all the way! Oh, what fun it is to ride in a one horse o-pen sleigh!

Duet Part (Play one octave lower.)

Review

1. This sign (treble clef) is called a __treble__ clef. This sign (bass clef) is called a __bass__ clef.

2. Name these rests. __~~half~~ whole__   __half__   __quarter__

3. Name these notes. __half__   __quarter whole dotted half eighth notes__

4. This sign ♯ is called a __sharp__ sign. It means to play the next key to the __right__ (left, right).

5. This sign ♭ is called a __flat__ sign. It means to play the next key to the __left__ (left, right).

6. Name these melodic and harmonic intervals. Play them.

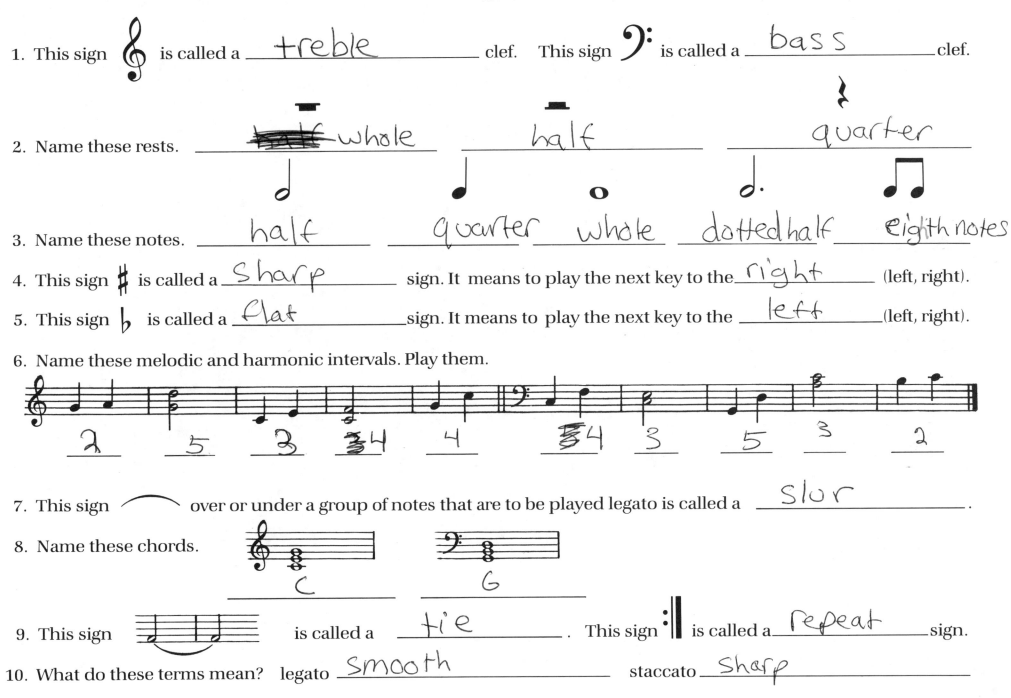

__2__   __5__   __3__   __3 4__   __4__   __5 4__   __3__   __5__   __3__   __2__

7. This sign ⌒ over or under a group of notes that are to be played legato is called a __slur__.

8. Name these chords.

__C__   __G__

9. This sign is called a __tie__. This sign ‖: is called a __repeat__ sign.

10. What do these terms mean? legato __smooth__   staccato __sharp__

Certificate of Achievement

This certifies that

_____

has completed

Piano, Primer Level

of

Bastien Piano Basics

and is promoted to Level 1.

This certificate is given in recognition of this significant achievement.

Date_____   Teacher_____